JUNIOR GREAT BOOKS

INTERPRETIVE ACTIVITIES

SERIES 6

FIRST SEMESTER

THE GREAT BOOKS FOUNDATION

A nonprofit educational corporation

Copyright © 1993 by The Great Books Foundation
Chicago, Illinois
All rights reserved
ISBN 1-880323-51-6

First Printing
9   8   7   6   5
Printed in the United States of America

Cover art by Ed Young.
Text and cover design by William Seabright,
William Seabright & Associates.

Published and distributed by

The Great Books Foundation
A nonprofit educational corporation
35 East Wacker Drive, Suite 2300
Chicago, Illinois 60601-2298

THROUGH THE TUNNEL

Doris Lessing

Name: _____

What is something difficult or challenging that you have done?

_____

_____

Check the reasons that explain why you did this.

- ☐ To test or improve myself
- ☐ For excitement
- ☐ To feel more grown up
- ☐ To be accepted or respected by a group
- ☐ To compete against others
- ☐ To _____

Now discuss this question with your class:
How can doing something difficult change someone?

Name: _____

During your second reading of the story, you marked places where Jerry is acting like a **child,** and places where he is acting like a **grownup.**

Now look over your notes and write down what you think is the most grown-up thing Jerry does.

The most grown-up thing Jerry does is _____

_____

_____

I think this is a grown-up thing to do because _____

_____

_____

_____

_____

_____

_____

_____

Name: _____

At the beginning of the story, when Jerry's mother asks him if he is tired of the usual beach, Jerry says "Oh, no!" and smiles with an "unfailing impulse of **contrition.**"

> **contrition**
>
> ∿ a feeling of deep regret for one's faults or serious wrongdoings

What **fault or wrongdoing** does Jerry **feel regret about**?

1. _____

2. _____

How does Jerry feel he *should* act toward his mother?

_____

_____

Why does Jerry feel this way?

1. _____

_____

2. _____

_____

Now answer this interpretive question:

Why is Jerry able to overcome his feeling of contrition and tell his mother what he really wants to do?

_____

_____

_____

_____

_____

_____

_____

Name: _____

Make notes for a story about a boy or girl who sets a difficult challenge for himself or herself.

What are your character's strengths and weaknesses?

_____
_____
_____
_____
_____
_____
_____

Where does the story take place?

_____
_____
_____
_____
_____
_____

Your Story Idea

_____
_____
_____
_____
_____
_____

Why does your character take on this challenge?

_____
_____
_____
_____
_____
_____

How does your character feel different afterward?

_____
_____
_____
_____
_____
_____

Additional Notes for Your Story

Name: _____

Make notes for an essay that answers this question:

Do you think that Jerry's accomplishment of swimming through the tunnel was worth the risk?

Begin by writing down what Jerry **risks** and **gains** when he does each of the following things.

Devotes his whole vacation to rigorous training

What Jerry risks: _____

_____

_____

_____

What Jerry gains: _____

_____

_____

_____

Doesn't tell his mother what he does every day at the rocks

What Jerry risks: _____

_____

_____

_____

What Jerry gains: _____

_____

_____

_____

Swims through the tunnel, instead of waiting until next year

What Jerry risks: _____

_____

_____

_____

What Jerry gains: _____

_____

_____

_____

Other things Jerry risks or gains:

_____

_____

_____

_____

_____

_____

Now look over the risks and gains that you noted and write down your conclusion. This can be the first sentence in your essay.

_____

_____

_____

_____

_____

RAYMOND'S RUN

Toni Cade Bambara

Name: _____

Think about each situation and check your answer.

	Probably	Probably not
If you were choosing people for a ball team, would you pick your best friend instead of the best player to avoid hurting your friend's feelings?	☐	☐
Would you back down from an argument just to keep the peace?	☐	☐
Would you spend time with someone you didn't like because your mother asked you to?	☐	☐

Now discuss this question with your class:
Are girls expected to be nicer than boys?

Name: _____

During your second reading of the story, you marked places where Squeaky's attitude or opinion about something **helps** her or **hurts** her.

Now look over your notes and answer this question:
Do you think that Squeaky's opinion of herself as the "baddest thing around" does more to help her or to hurt her?

Be sure to give reasons for your answer.

_____

_____

_____

_____

_____

_____

_____

_____

Name: _____

After the big race, Squeaky and Gretchen find out that they **respect** each other. What makes Squeaky respect or not respect someone?

Squeaky **feels respect** for **Raymond** because _____

_____

_____

_____

Squeaky **feels respect** for _____

because _____

_____

_____

_____

Squeaky **doesn't feel respect** for **Mr. Pearson** because _____

_____

_____

_____

Squeaky **doesn't feel respect** for _____

because _____

_____

_____

_____

Now answer this interpretive question:

Why does Squeaky think that acting like flowers, fairies, or strawberries keeps girls from being worthy of respect?

_____

_____

_____

_____

_____

_____

_____

_____

Name: _____

Make notes for a monologue by an opinionated character like Squeaky who speaks out about something stupid or unfair at school.

Why does your character think that this thing is stupid or unfair?

_____
_____
_____
_____
_____
_____
_____

Why does your character think he or she is an authority on this subject?

_____
_____
_____
_____
_____
_____
_____

What Your Character Objects To

_____
_____
_____
_____
_____
_____

What does your character want to say to people who are in favor of this thing?

_____
_____
_____
_____
_____

What does your character think should be done?

_____
_____
_____
_____
_____

Additional Notes for Your Monologue

_____
_____
_____
_____
_____
_____
_____
_____
_____
_____
_____
_____
_____
_____
_____
_____
_____
_____
_____
_____
_____
_____
_____
_____
_____

Evaluative Writing

Name: _____

Make notes for an essay that answers this question:
Do you agree with Squeaky that girls have trouble being honest in their friendships?

How would you describe an honest friendship?

Why might someone think that girls don't practice "real smiling" with each other?

Your Opinion

How can adults sometimes encourage girls to be nice in ways that aren't honest?

Is it easier for boys to "be themselves" in their friendships?

Additional Notes for Your Essay

_____

_____

_____

_____

_____

_____

_____

_____

_____

_____

_____

_____

_____

_____

_____

_____

_____

_____

_____

_____

_____

_____

_____

_____

_____

MY GREATEST AMBITION

Morris Lurie

Name: _____

Imagine that you are going to be interviewed for a dream job, for example,
a park ranger, a fashion consultant, or a TV writer, newscaster, or video reviewer.
To prepare for this interview, think about these questions:

What would you wear and how would you act?

How would you convince the interviewer that you could do the job,
even though you are young and still in school?

What would you tell yourself to keep up your confidence?

Now answer this question:
If you didn't get the job, would you give up on your ambition?

_____

_____

_____

_____

Name: _____

During your second reading of the story, you marked places where Morris **shows determination,** and places where he **does not show determination.**

Now look over your notes and answer this interpretive question:
Why doesn't Morris complain when he is offered a tour of the factory instead of a job?

_____

_____

_____

_____

_____

_____

_____

_____

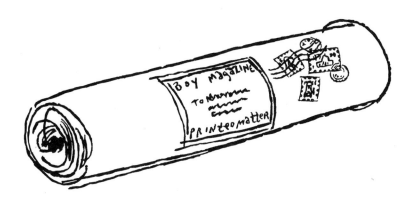

Name: _____

Morris introduces his father as a "great **scoffer**."

> **scoffer**
>
> § one who ridicules or makes sarcastic remarks
> § one who doubts the sincerity and good intentions of others

What is Morris' father trying to tell his son when he . . .

Says, AN APPOINTMENT? That means they don't want it. If they wanted it, believe me, there'd be a cheque.

see page 29

_____

_____

_____

_____

_____

_____

Calls Morris a "prince" when he is dressed up in his good suit with the yellow silk tie?

A PRINCE!

See page 31

_____

_____

_____

_____

_____

Holds the cheque up to the light and says,

We'll know in a few days if it's any good.

See page 38

_____
_____
_____
_____
_____
_____

Now answer this interpretive question:

Why does Morris go ahead with his plans, in spite of his father's scoffing?

_____
_____
_____
_____
_____
_____
_____
_____

Name: _____

Make notes for the feature that you will contribute to your class magazine.

Your department: _____

Your assignment: _____

_____

What is the main thing you want to tell your readers? _____

_____

_____

_____

How will you prepare to write your feature? _____

_____

_____

_____

What information will you include in your feature? _____

_____

_____

_____

_____

_____

Additional Notes for Your Assignment

_____
_____
_____
_____
_____
_____
_____
_____
_____
_____
_____
_____
_____
_____
_____
_____
_____
_____
_____
_____
_____
_____
_____
_____
_____
_____
_____
_____
_____

Name: _____

Make notes for an essay that answers this question:
Do you think it is good to be a dreamer?

How would you describe a dreamer?

_____
_____
_____
_____
_____
_____

Give examples of an inspiring dream
and a silly dream.

_____
_____
_____
_____
_____
_____

Your Opinion

_____
_____
_____
_____
_____

When do you think people should change or
give up on their dreams?

_____
_____
_____
_____
_____

Do you think that most successful people
are dreamers or realists?

_____
_____
_____
_____
_____

Additional Notes for Your Essay

_____

_____

_____

_____

_____

_____

_____

_____

_____

_____

_____

_____

_____

_____

_____

_____

_____

_____

_____

_____

_____

_____

_____

A LIKELY PLACE

Paula Fox

Name: _____

How do you think grownups should treat kids?

Should grownups help kids do things correctly, or let them figure things out for themselves?

_____

_____

Should grownups ask kids about their feelings, or leave kids to themselves?

_____

_____

Should grownups get mad when kids do something wrong, or act like nothing has happened?

_____

_____

Should grownups have high expectations of kids, or be satisfied with whatever effort kids make?

_____

_____

Name: _____

During your second reading of the story, you marked places where adults do things that make Lewis feel **discouraged,** and places where they do things that make him feel **encouraged.**

Now look over your notes and answer this interpretive question:
Why does Lewis like Miss Fitchlow and Mr. Madruga?

_____

_____

_____

_____

_____

_____

_____

_____

Name: _____

Lewis' parents want him to be **responsible.** But Lewis wants to **run away.**

> **responsible**
>
> ☂ trustworthy; dependable
> ☂ grown-up

> **run away**
>
> ☂ to leave home, usually in secret
> ☂ to go out of control

In what ways does Lewis show that he *is* responsible?

1. _____

2. _____

Why do Lewis' parents think he is *not* responsible?

1. _____

2. _____

How does a person who wants to run away feel?

_____

_____

Now answer this interpretive question:
Why does Lewis sometimes run away from responsibility?

_____

_____

_____

_____

_____

_____

_____

_____

Creative Writing

Name: _____

Make notes for a story about what happens when your parents go out of town for
a while and leave you with the ideal sitter.

What does your sitter look like?
How does he or she talk and act?

_____
_____
_____
_____
_____
_____

What unusual or fun things does your sitter do?
Do you do these things together?

_____
_____
_____
_____
_____
_____

Your Story Idea

_____
_____
_____
_____
_____

What does your sitter allow you to do that your
parents don't? Why does this make you glad?

_____
_____
_____
_____
_____

How does your sitter help you grow up a little?

_____
_____
_____
_____
_____

Additional Notes for Your Story

_____

_____

_____

_____

_____

_____

_____

_____

_____

_____

_____

_____

_____

_____

_____

_____

_____

_____

_____

_____

_____

_____

Name: _____

Make notes for an essay describing a special place you would like to have,
and how it would make you feel more grown up.

What does your special place look like
and how do you fix it up?

_____
_____
_____
_____
_____
_____

When do you go to your special place?
What do you do there?

_____
_____
_____
_____
_____
_____

Your Special Place

_____
_____
_____
_____
_____

Do you like to be alone in your place, or have
visitors? Would you like to live there?

_____
_____
_____
_____
_____

How does having your own special place
make you feel good?

_____
_____
_____
_____
_____

Additional Notes for Your Essay

_____

_____

_____

_____

_____

_____

_____

_____

_____

_____

_____

_____

_____

_____

_____

_____

_____

_____

_____

_____

_____

_____

_____

_____

THE MYSTERIES OF
THE CABALA

Isaac Bashevis Singer

Name: _____

In order to think about a story's meaning, we must enter into the world of that story. We must try to imagine what the characters' lives are like and see the world through their eyes.

Isaac Bashevis Singer's story, "The Mysteries of the Cabala," takes place in Warsaw, Poland, during the early 1900s. At that time, Poland was home to a large number of Jews, many of whom were members of the Hasidic sect.

Although the characters in the story are poor, they share a culture that is rich in ancient traditions. Almost every aspect of their daily life, including the way they dress, has religious significance. Following the Bible's commandments, the men and boys let the hair in front of their ears grow into sidelocks, and wear a fringed garment under their clothes to remind them of their commitment to God.

Rules and rituals are strictly observed. One important ceremony is the bar mitzvah, celebrated when a boy turns thirteen and is officially recognized as an adult member of the Jewish community. When young people are old enough to marry, a match would most often be arranged by their parents, perhaps with the help of a professional matchmaker.

As you will notice in "The Mysteries of the Cabala," Jewish culture places a high value on study and prayer. The rabbi is the religious leader and chief teacher of the community, but spiritual activity is an important part of everyone's life. In addition to the Torah—the first five books of the Bible—Jews study the Talmud, the teachings of the early rabbis. Hasidic Jews also read the Cabala, which is a mystical commentary on the Torah. Like many Jews, the narrator of "The Mysteries of the Cabala" believes that the true Messiah will one day arrive, announced by the prophet Elijah, and bring about peace on earth.

Name: _____

Invent a story about yourself and tell it to the others in your group.
Then discuss these questions with your class.

What did you like best about telling your story and hearing everyone else's?

_____

_____

Did you find yourself really *wanting* to make your story more fantastic than
the others? Why?

_____

_____

How would you feel if someone actually believed your story?

_____

_____

Name: _____

During your second reading of the story, you marked places where the narrator is confronted with something **mysterious.**

Now look over your notes and write down your own interpretive question and an answer. If you can think of a second answer to your question, write that down, too.

Interpretive question: _____

_____

_____

_____

Answer: _____

_____

_____

_____

_____

_____

_____

Name: _____

The narrator wants to learn the mysteries of the **Cabala.**

> **Cabala**
>
> 📖 a holy book studied by Hasidic Jews. The Cabala contains
> interpretations of the Torah by the ancient rabbis.
> They believed that every word, letter, and number in the
> Torah contained mysteries that could be understood
> by those who knew the secret. The names for God—and
> even the letters in the names—were believed to contain
> miraculous power.

Why does the narrator become frightened when he realizes that he has been
playing games with the Cabala?

_____

_____

_____

Why does the narrator's father try to discourage him from studying the Cabala
too early?

_____

_____

_____

Why does the narrator think that the Cabala might tell him whom he will marry?

_____

_____

_____

Now answer this interpretive question:

Why does the narrator feel close to madness when he begs his father to teach him the Cabala?

_____

_____

_____

_____

_____

_____

_____

_____

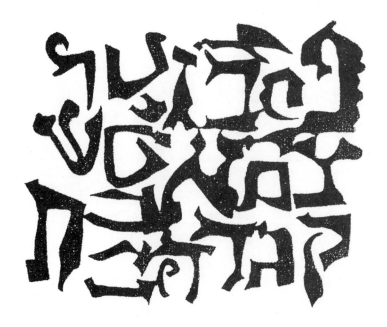

Name: _____

Make notes for a story about what the person you are going to marry—your future betrothed—is like right now.

Where does your betrothed live?
What kind of family does he or she have?

_____
_____
_____
_____
_____
_____

What are your betrothed's hopes and dreams?

_____
_____
_____
_____
_____
_____

Your Betrothed's Description

_____
_____
_____
_____
_____

What do you and your betrothed have in common?

_____
_____
_____
_____
_____

Do you wish you knew your betrothed now?

_____
_____
_____
_____
_____

Additional Notes for Your Story

Name: _____

Make notes for an essay that answers this question:

Do you think life is mysterious, or is it easy to understand?

What is the most puzzling thing that
you have come across in your life?

_____

_____

_____

_____

_____

_____

_____

Do you brood about this thing,
or do you feel it is not so important?

_____

_____

_____

_____

_____

_____

_____

Your Opinion

_____

_____

_____

_____

_____

How do you feel about the fact that it is
impossible for us to know everything?

_____

_____

_____

_____

_____

Do you think that growing up will answer
most of the things you want to know?

_____

_____

_____

_____

_____

Additional Notes for Your Essay

_____

_____

_____

_____

_____

_____

_____

_____

_____

_____

_____

_____

_____

_____

_____

_____

_____

_____

_____

_____

_____

_____

_____

_____

_____

_____

BAD CHARACTERS

Jean Stafford

Name: _____

Why do people sometimes have tantrums? Circle what you think is the most common reason. If you think of a different reason, write it down.

They want to make others feel sorry or guilty.

They are frustrated and need to let off steam.

It's the only way they can get what they want.

They have bad tempers and can't control themselves.

Another reason: _____

_____

_____

Directed Notes

Name: _____

During your second reading of the story, you marked places where Emily is **pleased** with her friendship with Lottie, and places where she is **troubled** by her friendship with Lottie.

Now look over your notes and write down your own interpretive question and an answer. If you can think of a second answer to your question, write that down, too.

Interpretive question: _____

_____

_____

_____

Answer: _____

_____

_____

_____

_____

_____

_____

Name: _____

Emily thinks that both she and Lottie are "bad **characters.**"

> **character**
>
> ✳ someone with an interesting or unusual personality
> ✳ the inner nature of a person, including his
>   or her moral values

What do you think is most **interesting or unusual** about **Lottie**?

_____

_____

What do you think is most **interesting or unusual** about **Emily**?

_____

_____

What do you think is most "bad" about **Lottie's character**?

_____

_____

What do you think is most "bad" about **Emily's character**?

_____

_____

Now answer this interpretive question:
Why is Emily convinced that she has a bad character?

_____

_____

_____

_____

_____

_____

_____

Name: _____

Make notes for a story about a person who fascinates you but who has the potential to get you into trouble.

What things about this person fascinate you?

_____
_____
_____
_____
_____
_____
_____

What things about this person bother you?

_____
_____
_____
_____
_____
_____
_____

Your Story Idea

_____
_____
_____
_____
_____
_____

What do you learn from your experience with this person?

_____
_____
_____
_____
_____

Why do you (or don't you) end up being friends?

_____
_____
_____
_____
_____

Additional Notes for Your Story

_____

_____

_____

_____

_____

_____

_____

_____

_____

_____

_____

_____

_____

_____

_____

_____

_____

_____

_____

_____

_____

_____

_____

_____

_____

_____

_____

_____

Name: _____

Make notes for an essay that answers this question:

Do you think of Lottie as a criminal, or as a child who steals only because of the way she grew up?

What is your definition of a "criminal"?

_____

_____

_____

_____

_____

What things about Lottie's life make it hard for her to follow all of society's rules?

_____

_____

_____

_____

_____

Your Opinion

_____

_____

_____

_____

_____

Do you agree with Judge Bay that the child who steals is on the way toward becoming a bank robber?

_____

_____

_____

_____

_____

_____

Could Lottie use her "genius" to change for the good?

_____

_____

_____

_____

_____

_____

Additional Notes for Your Essay

_____

_____

_____

_____

_____

_____

_____

_____

_____

_____

_____

_____

_____

_____

_____

_____

_____

_____

_____

_____

_____

_____

_____

_____

_____

_____

CHURA AND MARWE

African folktale
as told by Humphrey Harman

Name: _____

People sometimes use the words **warm** and **cold** to describe how situations or experiences feel to them. For example, a cold situation could be one that is harsh or difficult to put up with. A warm experience could be happy or comforting.

What is an example of a situation that you would describe as **warm**?

_____

_____

What is an example of a situation that you would describe as **cold**?

_____

_____

Now discuss this question with your class:
Why do we need both warm and cold experiences in our lives?

Name: _____

During your second reading of the story, you marked places where someone
is being **cruel, kind,** or **indifferent.**

Now look over your notes and write down your own interpretive question
and an answer. If you can think of a second answer to your question,
write that down, too.

Interpretive question: _____

_____

_____

_____

Answer: _____

_____

_____

_____

_____

_____

_____

_____

Name: _____

Chura and Marwe have many reasons to feel **despair,** but they eventually find happiness because they are **faithful.**

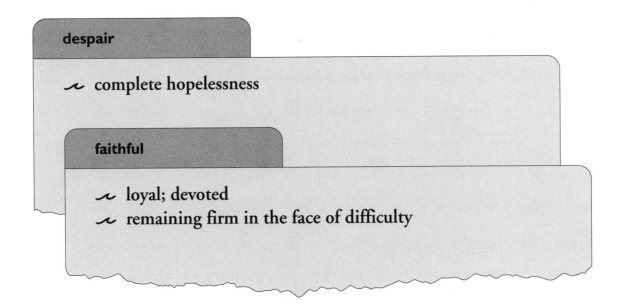

despair

~ complete hopelessness

faithful

~ loyal; devoted
~ remaining firm in the face of difficulty

What are some things that happen to **Marwe** that could cause her to **lose hope?**

1. _____

_____

2. _____

_____

What are some things that happen to **Chura** that could cause him to **lose hope?**

1. _____

_____

2. _____

_____

What does **Marwe** do to show that she is **faithful**?

1. _____

_____

2. _____

_____

What does **Chura** do to show that he is **faithful**?

1. _____

_____

2. _____

_____

Now answer this interpretive question:

Why does Marwe remain firm in her decision to marry a man named Simba, even though she will always love Chura?

_____

_____

_____

_____

_____

_____

_____

_____

Name: _____

Make notes for a story about someone whose visit to another world makes his or her life better in the real world.

What problems does your character have
in the real world?

_____

_____

_____

_____

_____

_____

_____

What is the other world like?
How does your character get there?

_____

_____

_____

_____

_____

_____

_____

Your Story Idea

_____

_____

_____

_____

_____

How does your character change in the other world?

_____

_____

_____

_____

_____

How is life different for your character when
he or she returns to the real world?

_____

_____

_____

_____

_____

Additional Notes for Your Story

Name: _____

Make notes for an essay that answers this question:
Are you a Masai "of sorts"?

What do you like about the Masai?
What do you dislike?

_____
_____
_____
_____
_____
_____

What do the Masai respect or love
that you do, too?

_____
_____
_____
_____
_____
_____

Your Opinion

_____
_____
_____
_____
_____

What do the Masai like to do that you
also like to do?

_____
_____
_____
_____
_____

What do you think the Masai would like
or respect about you?

_____
_____
_____
_____
_____

Additional Notes for Your Essay

_____

_____

_____

_____

_____

_____

_____

_____

_____

_____

_____

_____

_____

_____

_____

_____

_____

_____

_____

_____

_____

_____

_____

_____

_____

_____

SUPERSTITIONS

Mary La Chapelle

Name: _____

Epilepsy is an illness that affects the human nervous system. It can be treated with medicine, but people who have epilepsy may still have seizures sometimes or suddenly lose consciousness.

If you knew you had epilepsy, would you behave more cautiously, more recklessly, or the way you do now? Why?

_____
_____
_____
_____

If you had a brother or sister who had epilepsy, how much responsibility would you feel for him or her?

_____
_____
_____
_____

Name: _____

During your second reading of the story, you marked places where
Frances feels **strong,** and places where she feels **helpless or scared.**

Now look over your notes and write down your own interpretive
question and an answer. If you can think of a second answer
to your question, write that down, too.

Interpretive question: _____

_____

_____

_____

Answer: _____

_____

_____

_____

_____

_____

_____

_____

Name: _____

Frances' mother tells her that the rules she makes up are "just **superstitions.**"

> **superstitions**
>
> ↗ irrational or excessive fears
> ↗ illogical things people do to deal with their fears

What are some **irrational or excessive fears** that Frances has?

1. _____

_____

2. _____

_____

What are some **reasonable fears** that Frances has?

1. _____

_____

2. _____

_____

Even though it is illogical, why might Frances feel that her blind walk past the attic door helps her to **deal with her fears**?

_____

_____

_____

_____

Now answer this question:

Do you agree with Frances' mother that we all make up our own superstitions at one time or other?

Be sure to give reasons for your answer.

_____

_____

_____

_____

_____

_____

_____

_____

Name: _____

Include the answers to these questions when you write "The Sibling Pledge."

**What do you want or expect
from your sibling?**

**What don't you want your
sibling to do?**

**How much responsibility do you
accept for your sibling?**

**What possessions should siblings
share with each other?**

**What experiences should siblings
share with each other?**

**Who is the leader, or are you equals?
Will this ever change?**

**How do you want to help or
support each other?**

**What do you want your relationship
to be like in the future?**

•〜 The Sibling Pledge 〜•

I promise _____

_____

I expect _____

_____

I hope _____

_____

I _____

_____

_____

_____

_____

_____

_____

_____

_____

_____

_____

_____

_____

Name: _____

Make notes for an essay that describes a time when you, like Frances, listened to your innermost feeling, and it turned out to be a good thing that you did.

When did you have this feeling?

_____

_____

_____

_____

_____

_____

_____

What made you trust this feeling?

_____

_____

_____

_____

_____

_____

_____

My Innermost Feeling

_____

_____

_____

_____

_____

What did you do as a result of your feeling?

_____

_____

_____

_____

_____

_____

Why did it turn out to be a good thing that you listened to your feeling?

_____

_____

_____

_____

_____

_____

Additional Notes for Your Essay

_____

_____

_____

_____

_____

_____

_____

_____

_____

_____

_____

_____

_____

_____

_____

_____

_____

_____

_____

_____

_____

_____

_____

_____

THE LAST GREAT SNAKE

Mary Q. Steele

Name: _____

A person's **honor** is his or her reputation or good name.
It is the admiration or respect that he or she has
in the community.

Why would it be a terrible thing to lose one's honor?

_____

_____

_____

_____

_____

What might it mean to say that a person without honor
"is like a bone stripped of its flesh"?

_____

_____

_____

_____

_____

Now discuss this question with your class:
**Why might an innocent person who had lost his or
her honor choose to go off and live alone?**

Name: _____

During your second reading of the story, you marked places where **evil** is stronger than good, and places where **good** is stronger than evil.

Now look over your notes and write down your own interpretive question and an answer. If you can think of a second answer to your question, write that down, too.

Interpretive question: _____

_____

_____

_____

Answer: _____

_____

_____

_____

_____

_____

_____

_____

Name: _____

By looking into the depths of a stone from the head of a great snake, human beings can see the **truth.**

truth
w _____
w _____

Why are the truth-telling stones clear and colorless and deep?

_____

_____

_____

Why do the stones have to be fed and cared for?

_____

_____

_____

What are some true things that you think people might see in the stones?

_____

_____

_____

Now answer this interpretive question:
Why are we told that it is difficult and dangerous for human beings to see the truth?

_____

_____

_____

_____

_____

_____

_____

_____

Name: _____

Make notes for your legend of the seven great snakes.

Did all the snakes have the same purpose and power?

_____
_____
_____
_____
_____
_____

Were the other snakes like Ulukini—beautiful, half-blind, isolated?

_____
_____
_____
_____
_____
_____

Why the Great Snakes Were Put on Earth

_____
_____
_____
_____
_____

What was the world like when the seven great snakes were all alive?

_____
_____
_____
_____
_____
_____

How did people find out about the great snakes?

_____
_____
_____
_____
_____
_____

Additional Notes for Your Legend

_____

_____

_____

_____

_____

_____

_____

_____

_____

_____

_____

_____

_____

_____

_____

_____

_____

_____

_____

_____

_____

_____

_____

_____

_____

_____

Name: _____

Make notes for an essay that answers this question:

Should Bala have sacrificed the last great snake in order to return to his family and village?

What is sad about the loss of the last great snake?

_____
_____
_____
_____
_____
_____
_____

How does Bala's return benefit his community?

_____
_____
_____
_____
_____
_____
_____

Your Opinion

_____
_____
_____
_____
_____
_____

Is human happiness more important than preserving natural wonders?

_____
_____
_____
_____
_____

Are human beings better off in a world without mysteries and legends?

_____
_____
_____
_____
_____

Additional Notes for Your Essay

_____

_____

_____

_____

_____

_____

_____

_____

_____

_____

_____

_____

_____

_____

_____

_____

_____

_____

_____

_____

_____

_____

_____

_____

_____

_____

_____

_____

GASTON

William Saroyan

Name: _____

Sometimes it's hard to say what you feel. When this happens, people often talk about other things instead of what is really on their minds.

Act out this situation in your class:

Two best friends try out for the swimming team, but only one makes it. Although they are both thinking about this when they next meet, they talk about one of the following things instead.

• A math test they both just took

• What the two of them plan to do on vacation

• A party they both went to recently

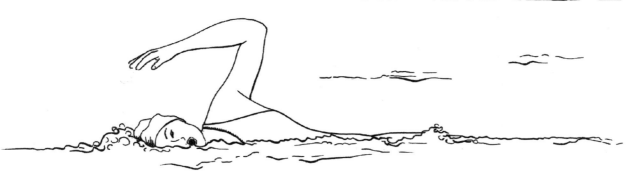

Now discuss this question with your class:

How did the friends express some of their feelings without bringing up what was really on their minds?

Name: _____

During your second reading of the story, you marked places where the girl feels **comfortable and taken care of,** and places where she feels she is **on her own.**

Now look over your notes and write down your own interpretive question and an answer. If you can think of a second answer to your question, write that down, too.

Interpretive question: _____

_____

_____

_____

Answer: _____

_____

_____

_____

_____

_____

_____

_____

Name: _____

The girl says that her father's **home** in Paris is nice, but that it is very different from the home she shares with her mother in New York.

> **home**
>
> ♦ a place where a family lives together
> ♦ an environment offering security and happiness

How do you think the girl's life in her New York home is different from life in her Paris home?

In New York, she _____

_____

_____

In Paris, she _____

_____

_____

Which home do you think would give **the girl** the most **happiness and security**?

_____

Why? _____

_____

_____

_____

Why *wouldn't* the New York home give **the father happiness and security**?

_____

_____

_____

_____

Now answer this interpretive question:

Why does the girl think that her father's home is like Gaston's?

_____

_____

_____

_____

_____

_____

_____

_____

Name: _____

Make notes for a story that presents an "ugh" creature as an interesting and appealing character.

What kind of home and humanlike way of life does your creature have?

_____
_____
_____
_____
_____
_____
_____

How would you describe your creature's "pure design and handsome form"?

_____
_____
_____
_____
_____
_____
_____

Your Creature and Its Name

_____
_____
_____
_____
_____
_____

What admirable qualities does your creature have?

_____
_____
_____
_____
_____
_____
_____

What happens to your creature that is like something that could happen to a person?

_____
_____
_____
_____
_____
_____
_____

Additional Notes for Your Story

Name: _____

Make notes for an essay that answers this question:

Does the father try hard enough to stay close to the girl, or does he give up too easily?

What does the father do to make the girl
feel close to him?

_____
_____
_____
_____
_____
_____

What more could the father have done to
make the girl feel close to him?

_____
_____
_____
_____
_____
_____

Your Opinion

_____
_____
_____
_____
_____

Is the girl better off leaving Paris with the
feeling that her father is a stranger?

_____
_____
_____
_____
_____
_____

Is the best way to deal with a forceful person
like the mother just to let her have her way?

_____
_____
_____
_____
_____
_____

Additional Notes for Your Essay

_____

_____

_____

_____

_____

_____

_____

_____

_____

_____

_____

_____

_____

_____

_____

_____

_____

_____

_____

_____

_____

_____

_____

_____

_____

SOUMCHI

(Chapters 1-5)

Amos Oz

Name: _____

"Soumchi" takes place in the city of Jerusalem during the mid-1940s, just before the nation of Israel was created. Answering these questions will help you understand what was happening in the city at this important time in Israel's history.

Why did so many European Jews leave their homes and move to Jerusalem in the 1920s and 1930s?

_____

_____

_____

_____

_____

_____

_____

_____

_____

_____

Why were British soldiers occupying Jerusalem in the mid-1940s?

_____

_____

_____

_____

_____

_____

_____

_____

_____

_____

What was the Jewish underground resistance movement? Why didn't all the Jews in Jerusalem support this movement?

_____

_____

_____

_____

_____

_____

_____

_____

_____

_____

Name: _____

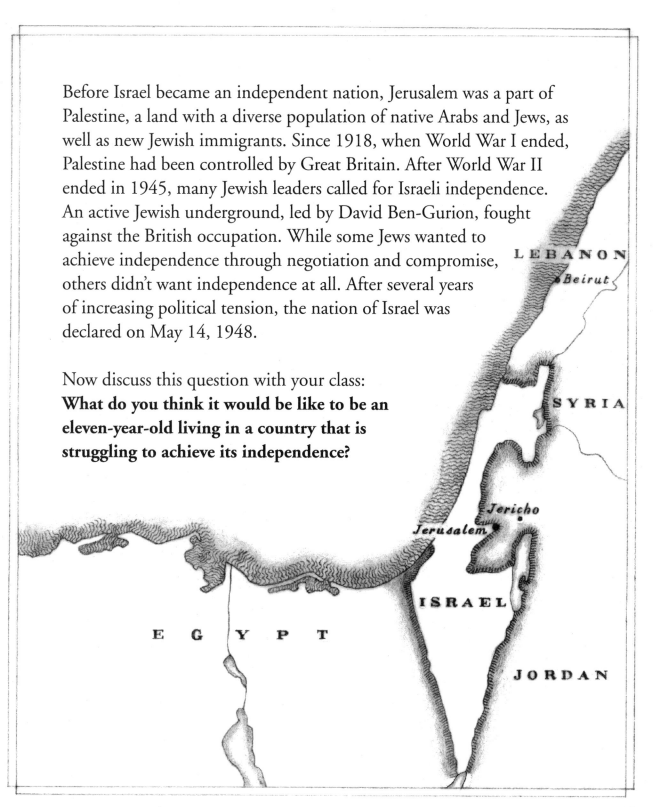

Before Israel became an independent nation, Jerusalem was a part of Palestine, a land with a diverse population of native Arabs and Jews, as well as new Jewish immigrants. Since 1918, when World War I ended, Palestine had been controlled by Great Britain. After World War II ended in 1945, many Jewish leaders called for Israeli independence. An active Jewish underground, led by David Ben-Gurion, fought against the British occupation. While some Jews wanted to achieve independence through negotiation and compromise, others didn't want independence at all. After several years of increasing political tension, the nation of Israel was declared on May 14, 1948.

Now discuss this question with your class:
What do you think it would be like to be an eleven-year-old living in a country that is struggling to achieve its independence?

Name: _____

During your second reading of the story, you marked places where you think Soumchi is acting **crazy,** and places where you think he is acting like a **normal** eleven-year-old.

Now look over your notes and write down your own interpretive question and an answer. If you can think of a second answer to your question, write that down, too.

Interpretive question: _____

_____

_____

_____

Answer: _____

_____

_____

_____

_____

_____

_____

_____

Name: _____

On the day that Soumchi gains and loses a bicycle, a toy railway, and a dog,
he says that he "**changed** completely, four or five times."

change

🐕 to become different
🐕 to replace one thing with another

How does the bicycle make Soumchi feel like a **different** person?

_____

_____

_____

_____

How does the toy railway make Soumchi feel like a **different** person?

_____

_____

_____

_____

How does the dog Keeper make Soumchi feel like a **different** person?

_____

_____

_____

_____

_____

Now answer this interpretive question:
**Why does Soumchi feel sorry that everything in the
world keeps changing, even though he is happy
to change his possessions?**

_____

_____

_____

_____

_____

_____

_____

_____

Name: _____

Make notes for a "verbal snapshot" of a memorable moment in your life.

What is especially memorable about your subject?

_____
_____
_____
_____
_____
_____
_____

What do you hear or see when you think of your subject?

_____
_____
_____
_____
_____
_____

The Subject of Your Verbal Snapshot

_____
_____
_____
_____
_____
_____

What smells and tastes do you experience?

_____
_____
_____
_____
_____
_____

What feelings do you want to communicate?

_____
_____
_____
_____
_____
_____

Additional Notes

_____

_____

_____

_____

_____

_____

_____

_____

_____

_____

_____

_____

_____

_____

_____

_____

_____

_____

_____

_____

_____

_____

_____

_____

Name: _____

Make notes for an essay about a special possession that made you feel like a different person.

How did you get it?

_____
_____
_____
_____
_____
_____
_____

How did it make you feel different? Did it change you permanently or only briefly?

_____
_____
_____
_____
_____
_____
_____

Your Special Possession

_____
_____
_____
_____
_____
_____

What things were you able to do with it?

_____
_____
_____
_____
_____
_____

What dreams did you make up about it?

_____
_____
_____
_____
_____
_____

Additional Notes for Your Essay

_____
_____
_____
_____
_____
_____
_____
_____
_____
_____
_____
_____
_____
_____
_____
_____
_____
_____
_____
_____
_____
_____
_____
_____
_____
_____

SOUMCHI

(Chapters 6-7)

Amos Oz

Name: _____

Which of these ways would you choose to show love to someone else?

Giving gifts	**Writing poems**
Teasing	**Sharing your secrets**

Now discuss this question with your class:
Why might a person choose each of these ways to show love?

Name: _____

During your second reading of the story, you marked places where Soumchi
loses or gives up something, and places where he **finds or gains** something.

Now look over your notes and write down your own interpretive question
and an answer. If you can think of a second answer to your question,
write that down, too.

Interpretive question: _____

_____

_____

_____

Answer: _____

_____

_____

_____

_____

_____

_____

_____

Name: _____

Soumchi introduces each chapter of his story with a summary of what will happen in it. In these introductions he sometimes refers to people and events from the Bible.

Soumchi writes that in Chapter 5 "King Saul loses his father's asses and then finds a kingdom."

What fateful thing happened to Saul when he went looking for his father's asses? (Read 1 Samuel 9:1-10, 9:15-21, and 10:1-2.)

_____

_____

_____

Why does Soumchi think about King Saul here?

_____

_____

_____

_____

_____

Soumchi writes that in Chapter 6 "I resolve to climb the Mountains of Moab and gaze upon the Himalayas."

Why did Moses climb the Mountains of Moab?
(Read Deuteronomy 34:1-8.)

_____

_____

_____

Why does Soumchi think about Moses climbing the Mountains of Moab here?

_____

_____

_____

_____

Now answer this interpretive question:
Why does Soumchi refer to the lives of great Biblical heroes to explain his own experiences?

_____

_____

_____

_____

_____

_____

_____

_____

Name: _____

Make notes for a poem about a marvelous faraway place that captures
your imagination.

What are some unique features of this place?

_____

_____

_____

_____

_____

_____

_____

What is mysterious or enchanting about this place?

_____

_____

_____

_____

_____

_____

_____

Your Marvelous Place

_____

_____

_____

_____

_____

What feelings do you have when you
think about this place?

_____

_____

_____

_____

_____

Who or what lives in your place, or is it uninhabited?

_____

_____

_____

_____

_____

Additional Notes for Your Poem

_____

_____

_____

_____

_____

_____

_____

_____

_____

_____

_____

_____

_____

_____

_____

_____

_____

_____

_____

_____

_____

_____

_____

_____

_____

_____

_____

Name: _____

Make notes for an essay that answers this question:
Do you, like Soumchi, feel sorry that everything in the world keeps changing?

Why is change difficult?

_____

_____

_____

_____

_____

_____

How can change be good for a person?

_____

_____

_____

_____

_____

_____

Your Opinion

_____

_____

_____

_____

_____

What are some changes that you would like to see?

_____

_____

_____

_____

What things would you keep from changing if you could?

_____

_____

_____

_____

Additional Notes for Your Essay

_____
_____
_____
_____
_____
_____
_____
_____
_____
_____
_____
_____
_____
_____
_____
_____
_____
_____
_____
_____
_____
_____
_____
_____
_____